Rosie Sips Spiders

Alison Lester

For Lachlan

hachette
CHILDREN'S BOOKS

Work

Ernie is a wildlife photographer.

Celeste is a famous ballet dancer.

Frank is an astronaut.

Her Royal Highness Princess T

Rosie's Droving P/L from the Kimberlies to Kosciusko % P.O. Cooper's Creek

Ernest Zebratrak Photographer of Wild Animals

Astral Exploration with Frank.

Rosie goes droving.

Nicky is the doctor at the doll's hospital.

Clive bakes chocolate cakes.

But Tessa is a princess.

Home

Rosie lives in a
caravan.

Tessa owns a
castle.

Clive has a house
on stilts.

Ernie's home is a boat.

Celeste lives in a skyscraper.

Nicky lives on an island.

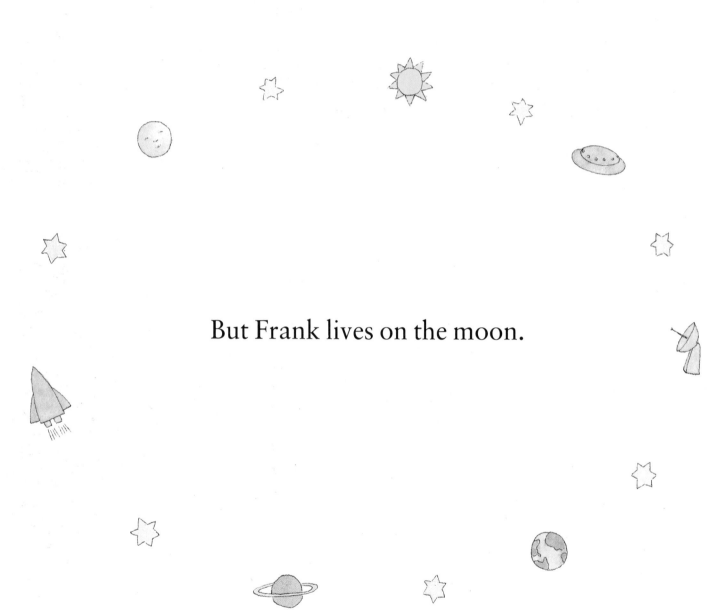

But Frank lives on the moon.

Favourite food

Clive eats fried rice.

Nicky loves spaghetti.

Celeste enjoys lemon-meringue pie.

Ernie likes roast
beef.

Tessa has Bombe
Alaska.

Frank eats space
rations.

But Rosie sips spiders.

Having fun

Ernie likes beach-
combing.

Tessa hosts the
royal ball.

Rosie sings with
her band.

Celeste feeds the ducks.

Frank studies astronomy.

Clive practises karate.

But Nicky loves to fly.

Gardens

Frank has a rock-garden.

Rosie tends a cactus.

Ernie collects carnivorous plants.

Clive waters a
window box.

Tessa has a maze of
roses.

Nicky grows
hibiscus.

But Celeste has a secret garden.

Animals

Nicky swims with a
dancing dolphin.

Clive has a baby
crocodile.

Rosie works her
cattle dog.

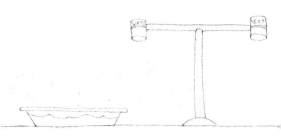

Celeste talks to her cockatoo.

Tessa has a tame tiger.

Frank has an ant-farm.

But Ernie has a menagerie.

Baths

Celeste soaks in her
sunken tub.

Ernie showers
under a tree.

Frank has a bubble
bath.

Nicky shares her
tin tub.

Tessa wallows in a
marble bath.

Rosie has a scrub in
the horse-trough.

But Clive jumps into Alligator Creek.

Sleep

Tessa stretches out on a four-poster bed.

Clive curls up in a sleeping bag.

Frank sleeps in his space ship.

Nicky's bed is out on the verandah.

Celeste has a heart-shaped bed.

Ernie snores in a hammock.

But Rosie sleeps beneath the stars.